To The Questioning Child

About the Author and Illustrator

Barbara J. Porter has taught English at Ogden High School and Bountiful High School in Utah. She has also written for the youth curriculum writing committee of The Church of Jesus Christ of Latter-day Saints. Dilleen Marsh's illustrations have appeared in the *Friend,* the *New Era,* and the *Ensign* magazines. Their first book together was the award-winning *Grandpa and Me and the Wishing Star. All Kinds of Answers* is their second children's picture book.

Library of Congress Cataloging-in-Publication Data
Porter, Barbara J., 1946–
All kinds of answers / written by Barbara J. Porter ; illustrated by Dilleen Marsh.
p. cm.
Summary: Explores different kinds of questions and answers, including answers to prayers.
ISBN 0-87579-538-2
[1. Questions and answers—Fiction.] I. Marsh, Dilleen, 1952– ill. II. Title.
PZ7.P817Al 1992
[E]—dc20   92-6976
                                                                                        CIP
                                                                                         AC

Printed in Hong Kong
10 9 8 7 6 5 4 3 2 1

ALL KINDS OF ANSWERS

WRITTEN BY BARBARA J. PORTER
ILLUSTRATED BY DILLEEN MARSH

DESERET BOOK COMPANY
SALT LAKE CITY, UTAH

Some answers are very loud—like
when you ask your mom if you can
have a pet snake.

Some answers are very soft—like when you ask the librarian where the books on dinosaurs are.

Some answers don't make any noise at all—like when you ask, "Can I get in bed with you?" and your parents scoot over to make a place just your size between them.

Some answers make you feel lonely—like when you ask your best friend to come over, and he says he's playing with someone else.

And some answers make you feel excited—like
when you ask, "Where are we going Monday night?"
and your parents say, "To the zoo!"

Some answers aren't answers at all—like when you ask, "Is it time for recess?" and the teacher says, "It's not your turn to talk."

And some answers are questions—like when you ask, "May I stay up a little later?" and your mom says, "Have you brushed your teeth?"

Some answers make you
feel embarrassed—like
when you ask your friend
if you can play with his

marbles, and he says,
"No! Last time you lost
my best shooter."

And some answers make you feel proud—like when you ask, "What did I get on the spelling test?" and your teacher says, "You got every one right!"

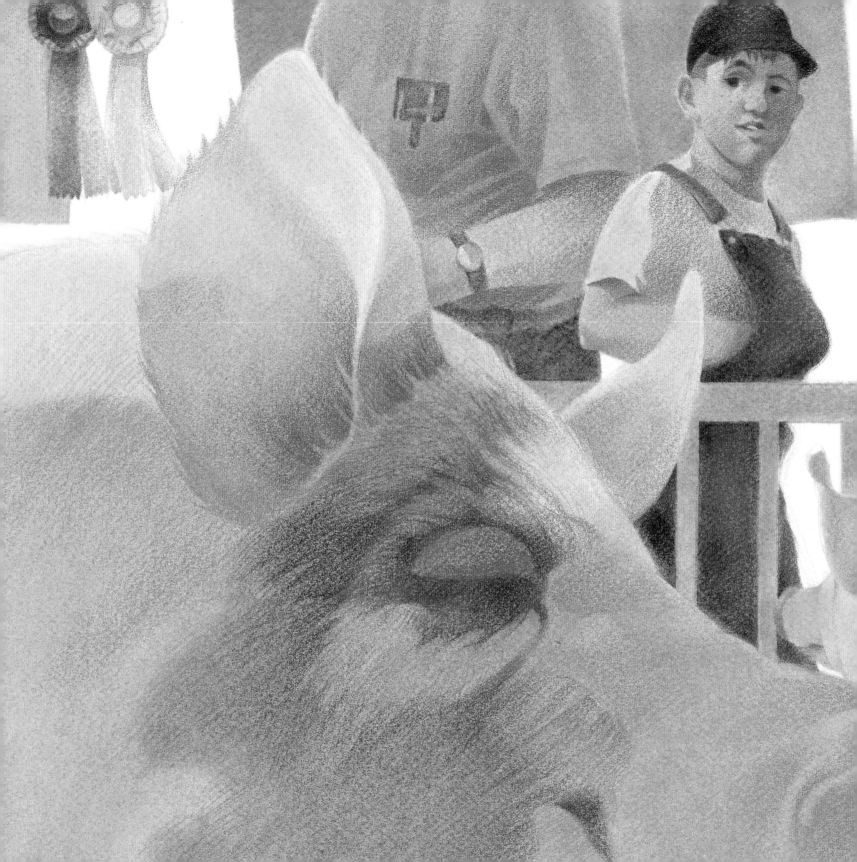

Some answers are silly—like if you ask, "When can we get a motorcycle?" and your dad says, "When pigs fly!"

And some answers are serious—like when you ask what happens to baby birds when they die.

Some answers make you feel kind of scared—like when you ask if it will hurt, and the doctor says, "Maybe a little."

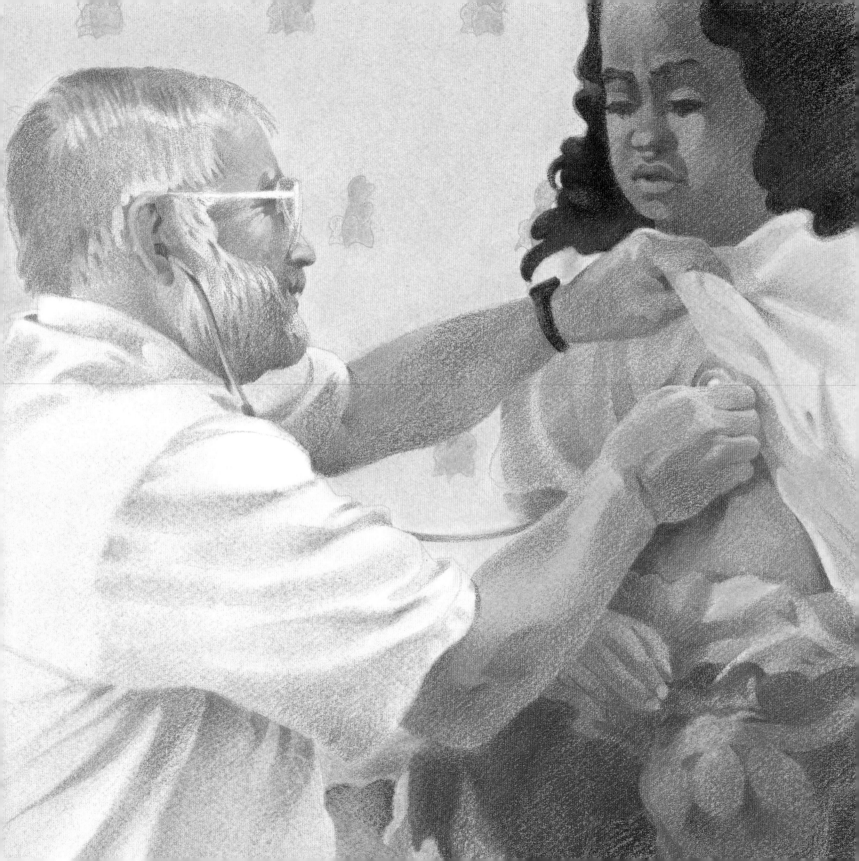

And some answers make you feel safe—like when you ask your mom if she'll be with you, and she says, "Of course I will."

And sometimes you need answers that only your Heavenly Father knows. You can hear him when you're very still and listen with your heart.

His are the very best answers of all.